Alistair Campbell

Series Editor: Andy Kempe

STANLEY THORNES (PUBLISHERS) LTD

First published in 1992 by Thomas Nelson and Sons Ltd

Cover illustration by Martin Berry

Typestyled by Peter Nickol

This new edition published in 1999 by:
Stanley Thornes (Publishers) Ltd
Ellenborough House
Wellington Street
CHELTENHAM GL50 1YW
England

99 00 01 02 03/ 10 9 8 7 6 5 4 3 2 1

A catalogue record for this book is available from the British Library.

ISBN 0-7487-4061-9

Printed and bound in Great Britain by T.J.International Ltd, Padstow, Cornwall

CONTENTS

SuperScripts

SuperScripts is a series of plays for use in the English classroom and the Drama Studio. The plays have been written by professional writers who share a delight in live performance and the challenges it offers to actors, designers, directors and, of course, audiences.

Most of the plays in the series were written for professional companies. All are included because they tell stories and use techniques which will interest, excite and offer new insights to young people who are just coming to understand how drama works as an art form.

The range of plays in the series addresses the requirement to give students at Key Stages 3 and 4 an opportunity to study a variety of dramatic genres. The fact that they were all written for performance (and have indeed all been performed) means that they will give students the chance to understand how and why playscripts are different from novels. The Activities presented after the script are designed to draw attention to this, and extend students' abilities in reading, writing and of course performing drama.

Many of the tasks invite students to engage directly with the text or formulate their own creative responses. Others focus on discussing, writing and designing. Both English and Drama specialists will find the series a valuable resource for promoting dramatic literacy – and simply performing the plays wouldn't be a bad thing either!

ANANSI

Anansi started life as a piece of Theatre in Education. It was first produced by Breakout and toured around primary schools in Berkshire. Like all good pieces of TIE, it aimed to help the young audience think about things in new ways. The company were faced with a problem, though: how do you get children as young as six or seven to realise what it would be like to be taken as a slave without terrifying them or just making them feel very sorry for the victims?

Throughout 1990 Breakout had been working with a number of story-tellers from around the world, and had invited Alistair Campbell to share with them his methods of working in drama with traditional performers in Africa. The company realised that the traditional stories people tell are a sort of coded history. They discovered that the lively stories of the West Indies and the old colonial states of the USA had been carried across the Atlantic by people who had been taken from their homes as slaves. The familiar tale of the tricksy Brer Rabbit (re-told in Walt Disney's rather sugary *Song of the South*), for example, is closely linked to African stories, not least the cunning yet somehow endearing character of Anansi – a spider who always seems to manage to survive no matter what.

The result of this research is *Anansi*. Although the play certainly gives an insight into the horror of the slave trade, its main purpose is to explore the value of stories as a way of coping with real-life experiences: as the Old Woman says in the play, 'I will teach you stories. They are a treasure no-one can steal, even if they have stolen your body.' By using these traditional stories, Alistair manages what may seem impossible: to write a play about cruelty and ignorance which is funny, full of hope, and celebrates people's resilience and capacity to learn from their past.

Anansi has undergone a number of changes since it was first performed by Breakout in September 1990. In 1991 it was extensively re-written for the London Bubble Theatre Company. The script presented here has elements of both performance texts.

ANANSI

CAST LIST

On the ship

Captain
Boy
Girl
Woman
Sailor
Auctioneer

In the forest of stories

Anansi
Tiger
Snake
Mancrow
Servants
King
Gran
Soliday
Patricia
Arabella
Bob
Ratbat
Monkey
Parrot
Centipede
23 Gerbils
Her
Cat
Dog
Crab

Anansi was first performed by Breakout Theatre in Education Company in September 1990.

THE GOOD SHIP HOPE. WEST AFRICAN COAST. 1791

THE CABIN

*Listen... hear the last sounds of a ship preparing for the Atlantic voyage. The **Boy** is seated at a desk, reading and writing. His father, the **Captain** consults ledgers and maps.*

BOY Father, why do I have to study when everyone else is up on deck?

CAPTAIN Silence, boy, and look to your books.

BOY But Father, I still don't see how all those people on the shore can be a cargo.

CAPTAIN Books or no books you have a lot to learn on this voyage. Look to it and do not bother me with damn fool questions.

BOY But who are the people on the shore, Father?

CAPTAIN You are on a serious trading venture whilst you are on my ship, and as the ship's boy you'll address me as Captain, especially in front of the ratings. You'll learn all about the cargo and such soon enough.

BOY They looked just like people to me. But they were tied together. They looked frightened. Why...?

CAPTAIN (*Cutting him off.*) I do not have to give you explanations. I am your father.

BOY I thought you said your name was Captain.

CAPTAIN (*Hits him.*) You young pup! Have that for your cheek. And there's worse waiting for you when you get down below.

On Deck

*Look... a **Girl** is waiting to be taken below. She is terrified. She stands, tied to several others. She calls out to deckhands as they pass. But they don't understand her language. They don't look at her or slow down.*

Girl Where are we? Are we going to die? What is this place, with all the people tied together and so much crying and fear? And why has the world come to an end? Blue, blue nothingness. Water, waves and more water. The water reaches up and touches the sky. Where is my mother? Where did all the pale men come from? Why don't you answer me?

Sailor Come along my beauty. Less jabber and down the hatch with you. I don't know! At least a bale of cotton doesn't chatter in some heathen tongue, and whatever it is you're blathering about you'll have to get yourself down this hatch. Can't throw you and damage the goods eh? Move!

He bundles her down the hatch.

The Cabin

Boy (*Reading.*) Yesterday we put in to the West African coast for the last time before the long haul to the Indies. I was looking forward to coming on this trip with Father: I really was. I thought we'd be away for a few months, and I knew we'd be coming back to Bristol with Rum and Coffee. I did not think to be so puzzled. No answers come to my questions. Who were those people on the shore? Herded together like cattle. Some of them were crying and falling down with fear. Some were whipped and beaten. One old woman was standing stiff and proud, with her hands tied, waiting her turn to be loaded aboard. She looked so calm as if she'd done it all before and didn't care. But she can't have, can she? They brought them down the river from far away upstream, and she can't have seen the sea, even, until just then. She caught my eye but turned away. She reminded me of Grandmama.

Dear Diary, you're my only friend on this ship. There's one Sailor who teaches me knots and talks to me. I shall tell you all my secret thoughts if Father gives me the chance from time to time.

The Hold

*It is almost completely dark, but look... The outline of hundreds of people packed together in rows on the floor, lying on narrow shelves that line the walls. Some are tied back to back to an upright beam. One of them is the **Girl**. A little light filters down from a crack in the roof. Behind her is the dim outline of someone tied to the other side of the beam. We will hear but never see this person.*

Girl I remember the river, carrying me further and further away from my mother on its great brown back. They tied us together. I don't know why.

They threw us into a huge canoe, bigger than the biggest war canoe of our tribe, and I didn't know why.

The jungle slid past. Two green walls of giant trees. We lay in the bottom of the boat, tied together like goats waiting for the knife, and I didn't know why.

Now all I see are people tied together, chained together, crushed together in the dark. It's so dark, Mama, like the big hut with no windows where the tribe stores the grain. Everyone is lying in filth and sickness and fear. Please, please come and hold me, Mama. Tell me this isn't true.

WOMAN What's true is true. Don't fight it. You're alive and it's true. It's true.

GIRL Who are you? I can feel your warmth but I can't see you.

WOMAN I am who I am, and you are who you are. No amount of fear and darkness can change that truth. Hold on to it! Hold on!

THE CABIN

CAPTAIN Dictation.

BOY Yes, Captain.

CAPTAIN Our last port of call on the African coast. Only three slaves of the last batch of forty have died on the six day river passage. May God be thanked for it. We have branded and documented and all slaves are now insured against death on route to the Indies. They are to be exercised daily in the hope that fresh air will reduce disease. One cup of maize porridge per slave per day should ensure that stores are sufficient for the voyage.

That'll be all.

BOY Yes Captain.

THE HOLD

Listen. A ***Girl*** *is crying. Crying in the darkness.*

WOMAN Child. Child. Listen to me. Don't waste your tears. You owe it to your ancestors to live.

GIRL I just want my Mama. I don't know where I am. Oh, please help me! Please!

SAILOR (*From above.*) Shut your noise down there!

WOMAN And how can you or I help each other?

GIRL I don't know! I am so frightened! I am sitting in my own filthy mess.

The two women sit quietly for a moment.

WOMAN Riddle me this, riddle me that.

GIRL Are you telling me a riddle? My grandmother does that, too.

WOMAN Riddle me this, riddle me that.

GIRL What is your riddle?

WOMAN What part of you stays free when your arms and legs are tied?

GIRL But all of me is tied. None of me is free.

WOMAN Think, child, think.

GIRL But I'm scared! I think I might go mad! I think I want to die!

WOMAN Tell me what you see!

GIRL Just what you see. Only dark. Why do you ask me when you see the same as I do... nothing.

WOMAN Only nothing?

GIRL You know what I can see. Rows and rows of people. Men, women and children. Piled up like wood for fire.

WOMAN And what else?

GIRL Why are you asking me these things?

WOMAN Don't question your elders! Tell me what you see.

GIRL I see a little light. Just a little light through a crack in the roof. Like light through the leaves of a great dark tree.

WOMAN So what part of you is free?

GIRL Well... my eyes, I suppose.

Woman And what else?

Girl My stomach. I'm hungry. They give us so little.

Woman And what else? What else is free?

Girl I don't know! Why do you ask me such things? You're not my mother!

Woman Tell me what you see.

Girl Ooh. I hate spiders. Sometimes they make webs in the roof of our hut. And I get my mother to throw them outside. And if she's not there I get a big stone and I squash them dead and flat. Squish!

Woman And do you see a spider?

Girl Yes. Why else would I talk about him?

Woman Tell me what he is doing.

Girl Why? What for?

Woman Just to pass the time...

The Cabin

Captain Take this log entry, Boy, and then you can help in the hold.

Boy What's to be done in the hold, Captain?

Captain One thing at a time.

We have embarked for Jamaica without incident. As we earlier feared, the fever which was rife on the coast before our departure has taken hold on the ship. Crew and slaves alike are showing signs of infection.

Boy Captain, what happens to the cargo when we get to Jamaica?

Captain We auction them, and if this fever leads to depreciation, it'll be at a loss, though the insurance will provide at least some recompense.

Boy Who will be recompensed, sir?

Captain Our masters in London, so start praying they are merciful should we lose too many.

Boy Our masters, sir?

Captain Yes, boy, our masters. Do you think there is a man alive who has no master of one kind or another?

The Hold

*A **Girl** peering through the dark at a spider we cannot see. A **Woman** coughing. See how the same web links them all together.*

Woman *(Coughs.)*

Girl Are you ill? I wish we weren't tied so I could see your face.

Woman You are, so you can't. You'll have to use your ears for eyes.

Girl But that's impossible!

Woman Don't tie yourself up with words like impossible. Ears can be better at seeing than eyes can, if you listen and don't just hear. Now tell me: what is our Anansi doing now?

Girl Anansi?

Woman Anansi is the name of that spider.

Girl Look at him! He can hardly get his web started! He scrambles up to that beam, and then falls, and then he creeps up again, then he falls again, and each time he tries he can't get a single thread to stick to that beam. Why doesn't he just give up and start in a new place? Maybe he'll just give up and die...

Woman But he is free, and you are not.

GIRL But he's so little and weak. He doesn't know any better. Look at him! He's just trying and getting nowhere.

Wait! He managed! He got one little thread onto the beam! A little, little spider with thin, thin legs. Ha! Anansi. Who gave him that name!

WOMAN You may think he's too weak and small to have a name, but that little spider Anansi was once a king.

GIRL Only lions and elephants can be kings.

WOMAN And why do you say that?

GIRL Because they're the strongest and the most beautiful.

WOMAN Listen. I will tell you a story. An Anansi story.

THE FOREST OF STORIES

Imagine... A forest full of stories. It looks just the way you see it in your mind: A mix of fairy tales you heard as a child to high-tech cartoon fantasy. It is all places and all styles. In the forest of stories there is no such thing as time.

The girl is still tied up in the ship, but dimly through the trees we can make out beams, and ropes... or are they branches and creepers.

1 Naming the stories

Anansi I am Anansi small and quick
Some folk are bigger, but usually thick
A crafty spider's what I am
I'm never without the smartest plan
The smartest plan and the cleverest head
Is how I keep from getting dead
'Cos the forest is full of every kind
Of creature you can bring to mind
From Tiger to Rabbit to Snake to Bee
And every one is bigger than me
But how do I do it? Wait and see
I can teach you things if you listen to me.
Two legs to dance and two to run
Two are free for banana fun
And the other two apart from those
Are for scratching my head and picking my nose.

A terrible roar thunders through the forest.

Tiger comes this way. One false move and I'm dead. Tiger's so royal, Tiger's so bold, Tiger's so strong, that the flowers close up when Tiger comes by. The birds pretend to be closed up flowers when Tiger comes by. The monkeys pretend to be birds pretending to be closed up flowers when Tiger comes by. And the elephants...

TIGER Anansi!

ANANSI Tiger, Tiger, burning bright. You're the Boss by day or night.

TIGER Sweet talking me Anansi? Forget it. I've been thinking.

ANANSI Thinking? Well, that's big change for you, Tiger!

TIGER What do you mean? Answer me, or I'll pull your arms and legs and brains out one by one.

ANANSI Just that you're so busy roaring and stomping about the forest and being grand and frightening people and... that sort of thing. Not much time left to think when you've got that kind of schedule. You Royals have it tough.

TIGER I've been thinking about our stories.

ANANSI Stories?

TIGER The stories that will be told of our fame, our power and our deeds long after we are gone and (Heaven forbid) forgotten. They will be called Incredibly Grand Magnificent and Wise Beyond Belief Tiger Stories and I shall star in all of them.

ANANSI Oh, that will never do.

TIGER What do you mean?

ANANSI Too obvious.

TIGER I'll make toothpicks out of your ribs and a hat out of your bum.

ANANSI I just meant that if they were named after a less magnificent and heroic and unbelievable person than yourself, like Rabbit or Mouse or possibly even a little squirt like... me, then the people, all over the world, to the end of time, would be so amazed when they found out that YOU were the real star of the stories that they would be even more impressed, your Majesty, than they would have been in the first place.

TIGER You can make words stand on their heads, Anansi. But I won't let our stories... my stories... be named after you unless you do the impossible to prove you deserve it.

ANANSI The impossible?

TIGER Bring me Mister Snake, tied to a pole, and the naming of the stories will be yours.

ANANSI I'll bring you Mister Snake, tied to a pole, quick-quick, chop-chop, swift-swift...

TIGER Get on with it! Not that you've got a hope... (*He goes proudly off.*)

2 TRICKING SNAKE

ANANSI Now, Mister Snake is a clever man
But I will catch him if I can
He's wise and shiny, cool and long
Smart and cross and VERY strong
But though I'm tiny and he's big
Let's try him with a juicy Pig!

*Along comes **Snake**. Somehow, **Anansi** has found a pig which he leaves in the middle of the path with a rather obvious noose dangling in front of it which anyone with a long enough neck can easily avoid.*

SNAKE Yum, yum. A nice little tasty little, juicy little pig. What a shame someone has tried to set him in a trap for me.

Silly, stupid, so, so, dumb:
I'll just stretch out my neck and gobble 'um!

ANANSI Oh, nits, bugs and maggots! and blast as well! A better trap is what I need. Let's try him with a chicken.

*This time **Anansi** ties the string to a chicken, which he has amazingly found! He hides behind a bush with the other end wrapped around one of his many hands.*

SNAKE My, my, my, what a super, succulent, salivating surprise. What a pity it comes complete with a trap, yet again. I'll just slide my neck sideways and gobble 'um.

*All **Snake** needs to do is give the string a hefty yank, and **Anansi** ends up on his back in the path before him.*

ANANSI All right Mr Snake. I give up. It was the only way I could think of saving your reputation but it's failed and I apologise for any inconvenience caused.

SNAKE Reputation? What has setting silly little traps got to do with my supreme reputation?

ANANSI Well... now that I can see you close up, as it were, I'm sure that Tiger and Rabbit, Parrot and Monkey and everyone else in the Forest were wrong about you being so short.

SNAKE Short! How dare you! I am the longest creature in the whole wide world!

ANANSI Yes, well I know that now, and you know that, but everybody else decided that this year's prize for the Longest Creature of the Year should go to... no, I can't say it... you'll only be upset.

SNAKE Who? What? Who gets this prize instead of me? I'm the longest creature in the forest and everybody knows it!

ANANSI Well... we were thinking of giving the prize to that bamboo tree over there... not a very interesting choice, but the committee did agree...

SNAKE A bamboo tree! But any silly, simpering, snivelling little snit can see that I'm longer than that stupid tree! And I'm wise, and superior and intelligent as well!

Anansi Yes, but none of the committee are here to prove that to, and even I can't tell your real length when you're all coiled up.

Snake Oh, for goodness sake. Why do I have to do everything myself? Being the cleverest and most beautiful being in the entire forest (not to mention by far the longest) is so tedious sometimes.

Anansi Oh, it must be awful being as superior as you.

Snake Stop grovelling. Now here's what we do. You cut down the bamboo tree, tie me to it so that all my coils are stretched out, out, out, then you carry me to the Longest Creature of the Year Committee and I win. Is that clear?

Anansi Perfectly clear, Mr Snake.

Snake Well, hurry up then, I haven't got all day!

Anansi *ties* ***Snake*** *to the tree. Just as he's finished,* ***Tiger*** *comes back.*

Tiger Anansi, I don't know how you do it, but I suspect your methods are not quite honest.

Snake So, where's my prize?

Tiger Anansi, I don't know what Snake means, but the Stories we live in will be called the Anansi stories from this day on. As for you, Mr Snake, have you any idea how stupid you look?

Snake I'll get you for this, Anansi, you... you... Arachnid!

Anansi Using what for legs, my friend?
You're all tied up, you cannot bend
When you can squiggle from your tree
Then you can settle things with me
Your strings are tied, your trap is set
And scissors aren't invented yet.

And that, my friends, is why they call the stories after Anansi... that's me!

ON BOARD

The Hold

Listen... even in the darkest dark there is laughter.

Girl So Anansi was the weakest and strongest at the same time.

Woman Yes. You listen and you learn. When I was a child my mother told all the Anansi stories to me, and now we are together I will tell some of those stories to you.

Girl But you're not my mother.

Woman What good is your mother to you now?

Girl I don't know.

Woman Can she make you strong?

Girl The thought of her does.

Woman Listen! You must be strong the way Anansi is strong. Strong on the inside. And you do have a mother.

Girl But she isn't here!

Woman Africa is your mother.

I will teach you stories. They are a treasure no-one can steal, even if they have stolen your body.

Tell me what you see.

Girl No!

Woman Tell me, girl: tell me what you see.

Girl The beginning of a web in the dark. How strong those tiny threads must be for Anansi to swing from them.

Woman Strong enough, you see? From inside himself he finds the strength to make his web: just enough and no more. Enough is all he needs to catch a fly.

GIRL How did you know a fly was in the web? I didn't see it till you spoke, and you can't see the web at all!

WOMAN Do I need to see something to know it's really there?

GIRL No, I don't suppose so.

WOMAN So it is with strength.

THE CABIN

See how two men share such a small space. Miles and miles apart.

BOY (*Reading.*) Last night I heard them singing down below. The song was as deep as the sea, but warm, not cold. I don't know if I want to know what it's like down in the hold.

CAPTAIN What is that book there? The little blue one.

BOY It is nothing, Captain, just a kind of diary.

CAPTAIN A diary? That sort of nonsense is for lasses. Put it away and get on with your work.

BOY But you keep a diary, Captain.

CAPTAIN These are the ship's journals and accounts. The ship's log.

BOY But they still tell a story.

CAPTAIN The only story that counts, young man. The story that says that money makes the world go round.

BOY Is Mr Newton wrong, then, to talk of gravity?

CAPTAIN Smart talk me, young fellow, and I'll whip you.

BOY Sorry, Father.

CAPTAIN Captain.

BOY Captain.

The Hold

Girl Mother? Are you there?

Woman I was walking in the forest.

Girl But you're all tied up, like me!

Woman Weren't you listening?

Girl All I can hear is crying. People are getting sick.

Woman You must listen ever more carefully. Not with sick ears but with forest ears that hear the health of the sick and the last breath of the healthy.

Peer into the darkness. See, in the background, two sailors untying a body and dragging it out of sight. Hear their mumbled curses. What or who are they cursing?

Girl Oh, look! Mama, look! They're dragging away a man! He doesn't move!

Woman Silence! Don't let them notice you!

Girl But what are they doing? How rough and cruel their language sounds. Like animals!

Woman You're still not listening. Animals are never cruel. They only live, and die.

Girl Well, the pale men deserve to die.

Woman Who can say who deserves to live or die. Listen again. What do you hear in them.

Girl Hard noises. They act as if we aren't really here. If they try to drag me away from you I'll bite them till they bleed.

Woman Then they'll flog you, and what will you have achieved? Haven't you seen them flog the others? To them you're not a person, just a thing.

Girl Will they eat us?

WOMAN Not the parts you can see. They eat your soul and leave your body empty. I pity them. Live well, die well, that's all.

GIRL And pity them?

WOMAN Shh! Look, and learn.

*A **Sailor** and the **Boy** come past, but stop and look and say...*

SAILOR Now see this old 'un here, Boy. We have to keep an eye on her for the fever. If she looks any worse than this it's over the side.

BOY But why?

SAILOR Orders, lad. It's for the sake of the others. Come on with you. It stinks like Death's own backyard down here and you're white as a little ghost yourself.

They go on their way, brushing aside a spider's web as they pass.

GIRL That one was just a boy my age.

WOMAN They don't come in just one size, child. Even these great conquerors can't build a person from nothing. They grow just like you.

GIRL I know it, mother. That's our secret, like spinning the web.

WOMAN Now you're showing strength. Weave your little web, like a dream in the dark, and wait, wait, wait.

GIRL But what are we waiting for?

WOMAN Not knowing is part of the strength of it.

GIRL But they are throwing people away!

WOMAN Riddle me this. Riddle me that.

GIRL What is your riddle?

WOMAN Listen to my story.

THE FOREST OF STORIES

*In this story animals and people are mixed up together. **Soliday** and **Gran** are human, so is the **King**. **Soliday** is a hero, any hero you like.*

1 The World blotted out

Animals Leopards leap and bunnies bounce
Peacocks preen, flamingoes flounce
The Forest of Stories is alive
With birds on the wing and bees in the hive.
With a buzz and a flap we dance the day
We dance we dance our cares away
With a shriek and a squawk we dance the day
We dance we dance our cares away.

Thunder rolls across the darkening sky.

Animals Mancrow's coming! Despair and death!
Close your eyes and bate your breath!
Huge as horror, vast as night
Blotting the sun out, eating light
Close your eyes and bate your breath
Mancrow's coming! Despair and death!

*In comes **Mancrow**, as dark and huge and horrible as any of you would expect a creature called Mancrow to be.*

Mancrow Bring me your babies, bring me your eggs
I'll drain your skulls to the desperate dregs
I'll suck out your eyes and empty your veins
I'll guzzle your guts and I'll feast on your brains
I've eaten them old and I'm hungry for new
And once I've had them I'll devour all of YOU!

There is a lot of screaming and panic – just as you'd expect!

2 The Proclamation

Servant Hear ye! Hear ye! O yes! O no! O maybe!
Hear ye here and hear ye there
Hear left ears right here and right ears over there!

King O dearest friends...

Servant Ears of the living, ears of the dead...

King O public true...

Servant On either side of the average head...

King Shut UP!

Servant I was merely doing my job, sire.

King Yes, well, you've done it. Now scram.

Servant Typical.

King What was that?

Servant Mythical, sire, I said mythical.

King What is? (*He whispers to the* ***Servant****.*) Look. I've got the public to address here and they don't just sit and gawp, you know... as a rule...

Servant I said mythical, sire, this huge Mancrow bird eating up the whole world and everything... selfish, I call it...

King Don't tell them the whole proclamation! I'm supposed to be King! I am King!

Ladies and Gentlemen, good and true
Boy have I got news for you
Mancrow's back – as you have heard

(*He glares at the* ***Servant****.*)

That mythical, magical, murderous bird
Whose wings have plunged us into night
And fearful, fumbling, fidgeting fright!
Whoever can save us from this threat

In addition to untold wealth will get
The hand of my daughter and the rest of her too
If they can PROVE they're the one who slew
This horrible, hungry, hideous hawk.
Now, let's see some action and less fancy talk.

3 The Initiation

Gran Soliday? Soliday?

Soliday Here, Gran.

Gran But what are you doing? You've just BEEN out hunting!

Soliday This isn't ordinary hunting, Gran.

Gran Now, Soliday. I may be old and splintery-boned...

Soliday Gran...

Gran Don't interrupt me when I'm enjoying being a miserable old woman! I may be old and creaky-kneed...

Soliday Gran, I'm going...

Gran I may be old and...

Soliday No, really you're not!

Gran crotchety-fingered, but...

Soliday Gran, I'm going to help the King...

Gran I may be old and...

Soliday Look, I've said you're not.

Gran rustily-elbowed...

Soliday Yes, alright then, so you're a decrepit old windbag!

Gran Then let me look you in the eye. That's where the truth is. Stand up to me, and you can probably manage this scrawny old Mancrow and still have time to fetch me some mangoes on the way home.

Hold still. (*Looks him in the eye.*) You'll do.

Soliday Wish me luck then, Gran. I'm off to kill Mancrow with my very own bow.

Gran Wait. You need arrows.

Soliday Oh, I'll whittle them as I go along.

Gran No ordinary arrows will do. Wait, I said.

I'm a sharp old woman, as you know
And I've six sharp points before you go.

She seems to conjure from nowhere six spectacular arrows.

This is for hope: without it we quail
This is for wits: without them we fail
This is for fear: your fear makes you strong
This is for anger at everything wrong
This is your name, simple and true
And this is the secret held only by you.

Now go, without a word. You have everything you need.

4 The Battle

Mancrow Good morning to you, Soliday.

Soliday Good morning to you, Mancrow, bird of darkness.

Mancrow And how might I help you, Soliday?
It's far too late to run away.

Soliday Just sit still then, ugly one
And eat my arrows one by one.

Mancrow Pipsqueak!

Trying to kill me? You pitiful thing!
It's like tying up the night with a noose of string
Trying to shoot stormclouds with a straw
I'll skewer you through with a single claw!

*One by one, **Soliday** fires the arrows in the order given by **Gran**.*

SOLIDAY Take that!

MANCROW Your hope means nothing to me...

SOLIDAY And that!

MANCROW Your wits are far too wee!

SOLIDAY And that!

MANCROW Your fear is justified...

SOLIDAY And that!

MANCROW Your anger's empty pride.

SOLIDAY And that!

MANCROW Your name will be snuffed out...

SOLIDAY AND THIS!

MANCROW What's 'this'? Your faith? Your doubt?
Your sins? Your patience? Mercy? Might?
That's odd... I usually get this right.
Which means I'm wrong, which as King said
Means that I might as well be...

Thud. He's dead!

***Soliday** takes a feather. **Anansi** appears from where he's been watching and steals one.*

ANANSI If in doubt, chicken out.
If there's a prize, improvise.
When you've a thirst, get there first.
If there's liquor, get there quicker.

I am the man that killed Mancrow...

5 The Reward

ANANSI I am the man that killed Mancrow...

KING The day is saved! The sun is bright!
Weakness has triumphed over might!

ANANSI What do you mean, weakness? Getting this feather took me all I've got!

KING I know, dear boy, I know. And to prove I'm as good as my word allow me to offer in marriage my daughter Patricia.

PATRICIA But I'm married already, Daddy.

KING Very well, then: my daughter Arabella.

ARABELLA I'm not your daughter, I'm your Aunt.

ANANSI Couldn't we just start the banquet while you all sort yourselves out?

He starts to eat.

KING My daughter Lucretia. Where is she?

ARABELLA Mancrow ate her last week.

KING My daughter Anastasia.

BOB I'm not your daughter Anastasia, I'm your son, Bob.

ANANSI Look, I'm quite happy with just the huge banquet, really...

KING But what, pray, is this?

Enter ***Soliday*** *with a feather.* ***Anansi*** *scuttles off with the food.*

KING And just who do you think you are?

SOLIDAY I am the man that killed Mancrow.

KING I've heard that one before. Look me in the eye. (***Soliday*** *does.*) Oh. Then who is... and indeed where is...? Scoundrel! Imposter! After him!

*The **Servants** chase around the stage and come at last to a locked door. They bang on the door.*

SERVANTS Knock, knock.

ANANSI Who's there?

SERVANTS Never mind who we are, we're looking for Anansi.

ANANSI But how do I know who you are?

SERVANTS Ask us knock, knock.

ANANSI Knock, knock.

SERVANTS Who's there?

ANANSI I thought you wanted to know who YOU were.

SERVANTS NO! We want to know who YOU are!

ANANSI Knock, knock.

SERVANTS Who's there? (That's better.)

ANANSI Come in and find out!

They do, but...

SERVANTS He's gone!!!

KING (*Handing rewards to **Soliday**.*)
This is for hope: without it we quail
This is for wits: without them we fail
This is for fear: your fear makes you strong
This is for anger at everything wrong
This is your name, simple and true
And no-one can pass on your secret but you.

ANANSI (*Sneaking onto the stage.*)
Off they go to the wedding bed
Me? I'll stay just me... and fed.
Live on the outside, grab what I can
Be myself – quick spider man.

I am the man that killed Mancrow...

ON BOARD

The Hold

Girl Why does Anansi keep looking for trouble?

Woman Because if you have wits like Anansi you have to use them. Like a knife, you have to keep them sharp. And like a knife, you can use them rightly or wrongly: to cut bread with, to live, to kill, or to harm yourself. One little knife against all these men: that's all you've got. Keep it hidden!

Girl Mother?

Woman One more question, and that's all.

Girl What do they do with the people they don't throw away?

Woman Do you want to know the truth?

Girl Yes.

Woman They sell, they buy, they buy and they sell.

Girl I knew it.

Woman Then why did you ask?

Girl Because I want to know what's to happen to me. You see, Mother, they won't throw me away.

Woman Go to sleep.

On Deck

Smell... The salt of the sea crashing the bow. The clean fresh wind singing in the ropes. The putrid stench oozing up from the moaning grates.

The ***Boy*** *sits crying in a corner.*

Sailor What's all this? You're a lad, a big 'un an' all. You don't cry.

Boy I don't feel big.

Sailor You're big enough to birch, which is what Captain will do if he finds you here like this. You don't let your side down.

Boy But I'm not on anybody's side. Nobody's on mine.

Sailor Not now, maybe, but one day you'll be Management, and that's the right side to be on, I reckon. Better'n mine, at any rate.

Boy May I...?

Sailor Now there's no time for knot-tying, if that's what you're after.

Boy May I ask you something?

Sailor What can I tell you that you don't know already from your fancy books?

Boy That's not the same and you know it. Books don't listen, fathers don't listen. All I get is told things.

Sailor So what is it? I'll be flogged if I dawdle here all day.

Boy What colour is God?

Sailor (*Laughs.*) Blow me! If that doesn't take it for a question to end them all! What do you mean, lad?

Boy Well if He's a man like they say, only a man that's always good and never dies, then what colour is He?

Sailor All I know is what they told me as a lad, and that's that we're all of us made in His image.

Boy So that man they threw in the sea today...

Sailor Is that what you were crying about?

Boy Listen! That means that man looks just as much like God as you or I.

Sailor No, no. You're out of your depth there, Boy. Slaves are different... more like, beasts, or so they reckon.

Boy It isn't true! I saw a girl today, down... down there...

Sailor Your trouble is too much imagination. You think too much and some thoughts is plain dangerous.

Boy But she wasn't a beast! She was just like me!

Sailor I've no time for this. A man is a man and a beast is a beast. The good book says that men were given to rule over beasts as they see fit, and neither you nor I are free to question that. Now let me be. Beasts or no, I'm just doing my job, and if throwing away spoiled cargo is part of it, then who am I to argue. If you want to know more, young sir, ask yourself whose fiddle your father dances to and why he jigs at all. Aye, there's a God to be reckoned with!

The Cabin

Boy (*Reading.*) Today they threw a man away. The sea was grey, so was his face. But the sea looked angry and he looked like he was asleep.

Captain I warned you, boy...

He takes the diary and hits the boy.

Boy But those are my thoughts...

Captain I leave you to work on the ledgers and you betray me.

Boy Let me have it back, Father. Please.

Captain You'll take this book and you'll throw it overboard. Then I might consider forgiveness for that and your other acts of dalliance.

Boy But I haven't done anything!

Captain Precisely. You've been idling and chattering with the ratings. Every man has a place on this ship and you'll learn yours if I have to break your back.

Boy I didn't ask to come.

*The **Captain** strikes him again.*

Captain From now on you speak only when spoken to. Here. Say goodbye to your precious book. You will be on deck in five minutes.

He storms out of the cabin.

Boy Dear Diary. I'm throwing you away. And though you are not finished, I'll keep your story in my head.

The Hold

Cough, cough, cough. Hear the barking of an old woman who still has a story to tell.

Girl Mother?

Woman Child?

Girl Mother, are you sick?

Woman Don't fear for me. I don't, so no more should you.

Girl They're coming again. The big man and... the boy. Don't let them see you're sick.

*The **Sailor** and the **Boy** come by. The older man inspects the **Girl's** teeth and eyes, then turn to the **Woman**. Can you see the flash in the **Girl's** eyes as she tries to turn around? She looks right at the **Boy**. He sees what we imagine. As the **Sailor** starts to untie the **Woman**, the **Boy** crumples in distracting agony.*

Boy Sailor! Sailor! I'm sick! I need the ship's Doctor! Help me!

Sailor (*Grabs him roughly and hauls him to the ladder.*) Nowt but trouble, you are, and that's a fact.

Girl They've gone, Mother. (*Pause.*) The boy – he has a kind of sickness.

Woman Maybe so, maybe so.

Girl What did we do that they hate us so?

Woman Nothing. They treat each other no better. When they see us, they see the thing they fear the most.

Girl What do they see?

Woman Riddle me this, riddle me that.

Girl What is your riddle?

Woman So light you can barely see it. So beautiful no human being can hope to make one. Strong enough to hunt with, pure enough to see through, always being made again.

Girl Anansi's web!

Woman Good. You're growing. This is the little answer to my riddle.

Girl And the big answer?

Woman The big answer is the soul.

Girl Are we going to die?

Woman I've told you once before, girl; you're going to live.

Girl But I want you with me! You're my mother now!

Woman I'll be with you.

Girl How?

Woman Listen to my story.

THE FOREST OF STORIES

1 Down by the Pool

*Enter **Ratbat**, cool as ice singing snatches of ice cool songs.*

'She wore an itsy bitsy teeny weeny yellow polka dot bikini
That she wore for the first time today.'

'The heat is high, The heat is hot
A sweltering summer's what we've got'

But I don't need no fancy hat
'Cos I'm real cool And my name's Ratbat.

But what is that awesome roaring in the distance?

Here's Tiger and Anansi coming along
To interrupt my summer song
But I'm going to hide behind this tree
So they can't mess with me.

Tiger 'It's too darn hot
It's too darn hot...'

Anansi 'We're having a heatwave, a tropical heatwave
The temperature's rising, it isn't surprising...'

Tiger What isn't surprising, Anansi?

Anansi Why, it isn't surprising that you look so terribly hot Tiger. Stylish, magnificent, Wise Beyond Belief, but so, so, hot. But I can take you to a cool, cool pool, so cool you could lie there all day under the shade of the green, green ferns, while everyone else just sits and sweats and smells. However, if you don't know how to swim, you'll just have to stew in your fine fur coat.

Tiger How dare you! Of course I can swim. All Tigers are best at sport. Show me this pool and I'll show you a dolphin with fur and claws.

ANANSI Come this way... left a bit... right a bit... up this little bank... ta-dah!

TIGER Stand back while I dive magnificently in.

ANANSI Wait! Surely you can't go swimming in your good fur coat?

TIGER Why ever not?

ANANSI Oh, dear. I thought you knew. It'll shrink and you'll have to be ever so careful bending over for the rest of your life.

TIGER Oh, why do things have to get so complicated around you, Anansi? Here. Help me with my coat.

Anansi *unzips* ***Tiger's*** *stylish coat.*

ANANSI There now. Once you've taken all your fat off you'll be ready for the longest, coolest swim any Tiger has ever had.

TIGER TAKE MY FAT OFF!?!

ANANSI Well, everybody knows how delicious, how scrummy and how lipsmacking Tiger fat is.

TIGER So?

ANANSI And if there are any Three-toed Fat-eating Bloogers in the pool, you'll be a very thin tiger indeed for the rest of your life.

TIGER Hold on a minute. I don't usually do this. And turn your back, Anansi. How I do it remains a secret no matter what.

Imagine... Awful slurping sounds and a splash as ***Tiger*** *dives in.* ***Anansi*** *scoops up the fat and cooks it!*

ANANSI Salt and pepper, herbs and spice
Tiger fat is nice, nice, nice.
Fry it, boil it, stew it quick

Eat the lot and don't be sick!

Mmmmm... just as galumptuous as I knew it would be.

Tiger (*From the pool.*) ANANSI! Are you watching my fat and coat as closely as you can?

Anansi Oh, yes! Don't you worry! Couldn't get closer if I tried.

Ratbat *creeps out from behind the tree.*

Ratbat Here's my chance to make a kill
I smell grub, and I'll eat my fill
When Anansi's around you never know
Just which way the meal will go.

Yo, there Anansi! What's cooking?

Anansi What? Oh... nothing, Ratbat. Anyway, what are you doing up and awake? Ratbats only come out at night.

Ratbat Not this Ratbat. You see, what I crave, Anansi, is Cool, and it's too hot to sleep today. I thought I'd just stroll on down to Song City where things are cool even in the noonday heat. I'm talking serious partytime. By the way, who's that in the water?

Anansi Oh, nobody special. By the way, Ratbat, being so cool I expect you've got your entry all prepared for the Song Contest.

Ratbat Natch, man. Um... which particular contest, out of interest?

Anansi Oh, just the Best Song About Tiger Fat Contest. It's kind of... you know... exclusive, so I'd understand if no-one had bothered to tell you anything about it.

Ratbat Of course I know all about it! I'm a brilliant singer, me!

Anansi What, you mean Parrot and Centipede and the

Twenty-three Gerbils were just kidding when they called you a glorified rat with wings?

RATBAT I beg your pardon? I'll have you know, Anansi, that if Ratbats didn't sing they'd all have bashed their heads in long ago.

ANANSI And how d'you reckon that, then?

RATBAT Because they bounce their songs off trees in the dark, that's how.

ANANSI Oh, I see. That'll explain why Parrot, Centipede and the Twenty-Three Gerbils said that bouncing Ratbat songs off trees was about the best thing you could do with them, then.

RATBAT EH!?!

TIGER ANANSI! Do I hear someone else yelling in the region of my fat?

ANANSI Don't worry, Tiger, it's just an echo.

TIGER An echo of what?

ANANSI An echo of what? See what I mean?

TIGER OK, then.

ANANSI OK, then.

RATBAT Who IS that in the water.

ANANSI Who IS that in the water. An echo. Oh, stop confusing me, Ratbat. I've only got five minutes to find somebody cool as an icecube in a polar bear's pyjamas, otherwise my entry for the Best Song About Tiger Fat Contest will be a complete waste. I can't sing a note.

RATBAT Cool as an icecube in a polar bear's pyjamas? Why, that could almost be me you're talking about. Let's hear the song and I'll enter it for you!

ANANSI But I thought you had a song already.

Ratbat Oh, I can always bounce it off a shrub or two later tonight.

Anansi OK then. Here it is.

Yesterday this time me am yum Tiger fat
Yesterday this time me am yum Tiger fat
Yesterday this time me am yum Tiger fat
Yesterday this time me am yum Tiger fat

Ratbat Wow! Brilliant! I can sing that no problem!

Anansi Well you'd better be quick. Those Twenty-Three Gerbils don't hang around, and Song City's a good way off.

Ratbat I'll fly. It's the thing I do nearly as well as singing.

*Exit **Ratbat**. **Tiger** gets out of the pool.*

Tiger ANANSI! Where's my fat and my coat!

Anansi Oh, Tiger. I'm sorry. I must have dozed off.

Tiger ANANSI! I trusted you with my fat and my coat, and they've vanished.

Anansi But Tiger, I've been here all along, just like I said. It just got so hot while I was faithfully guarding your beautiful coat and your delicious... I mean your important fat...

Tiger You have five minutes to help me find what's rightfully mine, or I'll rip you into a million quivering shreds.

Anansi That sounds fair enough. Five minutes is a wee bit tight, but we ought to make it.

Tiger Make it where?

Anansi Just a hunch I had while I was sleeping. Here. Wrap your dangly bits in this banana leaf and follow me.

2 Song City

Can you imagine Song City? Yeah! All the creatures are there, assembled in the coolest possible way.

Monkey Like, hi there, Ratbat. What's doing. Up during the day?

Ratbat I'm here for the Contest. Sorry I'm late. Not used to flying in daylight and I forgot which way wasn't up.

Parrot What on earth are you talking about, Ratbat? And who let you in, anyway. Song City is only for those as cool as ice cubes.

Centipede Yeah, like drummers with more than fifty legs on each side...

23 Gerbils And backing vocalists with ninety-two paws for those more complicated jive sections...

Monkey And, my dear Ratbat, songs.

Parrot Glamorous songs.

Monkey Wicked songs.

Centipede Catchy songs.

Ratbat So a quick ditty about Tiger Fat would do, then?

Monkey I don't believe I'm hearing this. Whatever happened to love songs and operas about bananas... you know... relevant stuff?

Gerbils If you stuck to being nocturnal, Ratbat, your brains would stay at the right temperature and we wouldn't have to listen to you when we OUGHT to be rehearsing, or breeding or something.

Centipede Aw, give the little guy a chance. Look at his face. He looks like he just bashed into a really big tree, real fast.

Ratbat Yes, well that's called having feelings, actually.

Monkey Get on with it and we'll tell you what we think.

RATBAT Here goes...

Yesterday this time me am yum Tiger fat
Yesterday this time me am yum Tiger fat...

PARROT Pa! What do you think this is – an audition for 'The Jungle Book'?

CENTIPEDE Shut up, you overdressed budgie, and let him finish. I like it.

RATBAT Yesterday this time me am yum Tiger fat
Yesterday this time me am yum Tiger fat.

A terrible roar. It's ***Tiger****.*

TIGER So it was you! You're the one who ate my fat and stole my coat!

RATBAT Where's my prize?

TIGER Anansi! I've heard this line about a prize before. Are you sure you've got nothing to do with this? Anansi...? Where'd he go?

RATBAT Oh, Anansi isn't here, Tiger. I left him back at the pool.

TIGER That does it! I'm going to tear you limb from limb.

MONKEY Hey there, man, who are you? Your voice sounds kind of familiar, but I've never seen such a weird outfit in my life. Looks like someone turned you inside out.

TIGER WHAT DO YOU MEAN, WHO AM I? I'M TIGER! AND I'M GOING TO MAKE POT NOODLES OUT OF THE LOT OF YOU!

ANANSI *(Appearing out of thin air.)* But we've no proof that you're Tiger at all.

TIGER ANANSI! I knew you were behind this! Not only do you let Ratbat eat my fat, but you let half the forest SING about it! I'm taking you all to the Forestry Commission!

ANANSI Well, if you are who you say you are, this coat ought to fit. I found it hanging from a tree.

TIGER *(Trying on the coat.)* Well... ha... ha... as you can see I've lost a bit of weight...

MONKEY Better rest up for a few days, eat well and we'll forget about the whole thing.

TIGER But that's not fair.

ANANSI You can't eat water
You can't eat air
You have to live
And Life ain't fair.

TIGER But where does that leave me?

ANANSI Looking a bit silly, my friend.

TIGER I'll get you for this, Anansi!

ANANSI You'll have to catch me first. And it won't be easy if you keep...

***Tiger** lunges and falls.*

...tripping over your coat like that.

*Exit **Anansi, Tiger** in pursuit.*

ON BOARD

The Hold

Girl (Laughing.) I love that story! That's the best!

Woman It's all one story. Beginning, middle and end.

Girl But I don't see an end.

Woman Young eyes don't see an end. That's as it should be.

Girl What do you mean?

Woman Where's our little Anansi?

Girl I can't see him now. The big man brushed him away. It's just as if he was never there.

Woman But you can see it still, in your mind's eye. Can you see it?

Girl Yes, I can. I will always see it, and I will always see you.

Woman Well, then. I have no more to say. (*Coughing.*) Good stories leave pictures in your mind, and they belong to you for ever.

Girl And what about you?

Woman Riddle me this... riddle me that...

No matter where you are or who you are, this is the same home that all of us are going to, high or low, weak or strong, frightened or brave. Where the people are as good as animals and the animals are just as they always were.

Girl I know the answer, mother. Shh! They're coming!

Woman Let them come.

Girl But if they find out you are ill...

Woman And what can you do to stop them? My teaching

has ended and you must go on.

*A **sailor** drags her away. The **Boy** lingers.*

Boy You mustn't cry.

She turns her head away and sings to herself...

Girl Yesterday this time me am yum Tiger Fat...

*The **Boy** doesn't understand. He goes.*

The Cabin

Captain What kept you?

Boy Nothing.

Captain Nothing what?

Boy Nothing, Captain.

Captain Dictation. We have sighted Jamaica. Thanks to the grace of God we have lost only one hundred and fifty slaves and twelve crew on our seven week passage. We have it on good authority that the presence of maimed, defective or diseased slaves at the forthcoming auction might seriously lower the average price. I have no choice but to take the necessary measures to ensure that only stock of the highest quality arrive in Jamaica. The rest regrettably go overboard. (*He looks at the boy.*) My conscience is clear. I am doing no more than any good farmer to protect the best beasts in the herd.

He starts to cough violently.

Leave me, boy. I've to make the ledgers ready for auction. We'll be unloading tomorrow.

KINGSTON HARBOUR

*See... A **Sailor** swigging from a flask. The **Boy** walking upright and stern towards him.*

SAILOR Well if it isn't our young genius. Found out the colour of God yet?

BOY Yes.

SAILOR Now you should beware of blasphemy, Boy. It's bad for the soul.

BOY Is it?

SAILOR Where's the Captain? Are you doing his ledgers for him at the auction.

BOY He's sick. Yes, I'm doing his ledgers.

SAILOR Good lad. And here's to a good rest and a safe voyage back to England and civilisation.

BOY Goodbye Sailor. Thank you for teaching me how to tie things up with all those fancy knots.

SAILOR I knew we'd see a man in you. Look now; they're starting.

*The **Girl** and others are led up onto a platform.*

AUCTIONEER Gentlemen of the fine and distinguished town of Kingston Jamaica. Freshly arrived from the African coast you can see before you a fine and wholesome stock of the healthiest slaves in prime condition. You are free to inspect our latest cargo, able-bodied but not yet trained, and every one of them fit for a quick start on the plantation.

Now what am I bid for this young female. As fit for the fields as any young buck.

GIRL I don't understand what he's saying.

AUCTIONEER Now am I bid forty-five...

Girl I can see what he's doing, and that's enough.

Auctioneer fifty...

Girl I want to cry, but I won't.

Auctioneer fifty-five...

Girl I want to die, but I won't.

I want my mothers, the old and the new.

Auctioneer Going once... going twice... SOLD!

The scene freezes. We are in the Forest of Stories again. The ***Girl*** *steps down and begins to tell us a story.*

Girl Once upon a time there was a clever, tricksy spider called Anansi, who lived in The Forest of Stories. If he was hungry, he got what he wanted. So will I. And this is how.

In the Forest of Stories there's no such thing as time. And in that time, once upon a time, lived a mean old woman with a heart full of hate, a terrible thirst and a calabash full of other people's tears to quench it. Nobody knew her name, except her children, Dog and Cat and Crab. Now these weren't her real children, because her real children had run away from her long ago. And why? Because she treated them like slaves. Now look and listen what happened to her.

THE FOREST OF STORIES

1 Quenching her Thirst

Her Children! Come here while I give you your chores.

Dog Aw, but Mum...

Cat We haven't stopped all day...

Crab And my claws are worn to the bone...

Cat How can they be worn to the bone when they're bone already, stupid?

Her SILENCE! Do I hear complaining? Do I hear whinging? Moaning? Grumbling? Do I?

All No, Mum.

Her Then what's your problem?

Dog We were just thinking it might be more fun for you to have a new slave...

Crab He means helper...

Dog Yes... helper... around the house...

Her And why do you think that?

Cat We didn't think it, Mum, we saw it.

Dog Yes, we saw it in the calabash.

Her The calabash! How many times must I tell you that the calabash is for my use and mine alone?

Crab But we only had a tiny peek.

Dog And we've cried so long that we've no tears left, and your calabash is empty.

Her That does it. I'm very, very angry. And what does that make me?

Cat Thirsty?

Her So what must you do?

Dog Work.

Her And then?

Cat Work more.

Her And then?

Crab Suffer.

Her And then?

Dog Suffer more.

Her And then?

All CRY!

Her Fetch me my calabash! My tongue's like a blazing desert at noon!

They collect the tears and she drinks.

Her Not NEARLY enough! Come here, the lot of you!

All No, Mum, no, Mum, please...

Cat Wait, Mum! We've got a better idea!

Dog Have we?

Crab Shh!

Cat Listen to this advert.

'Girl wanted to act as helper to delightful old lady in woodland retreat. One entire hour free per week unless the month ends in a Y or an R. No experience necessary.'

Her Well, now. That sounds reasonable enough to me.

Crab Just as well, Mum, because we put it in the *Forest News* today!

Cat Just think, Mum: once you've got her chopping the wood...

Dog Building the fire...

Cat Grinding the millet...

Crab Fetching the water...

Dog Kneading the dough...

Crab Baking the bread...

Cat And putting your toast on your table...

Crab She'll be crying so hard you'll have a sloshing full calabash in no time at all!

Her Are you SURE she won't want anything in return? Like... what're they called... wages, or some such thing.

Cat Oh, no, no danger of that...

Crab We just put in a little bit about how at the end of the week if she manages to guess your true name...

Dog ...then she can have half of everything you own.

Her HALF! But that's outrageous! What has anyone done to deserve half of MY property?

Cat But she'll never guess your name, Mum, 'cos we're the only ones that know it. And we wouldn't tell, would we?

Dog Nope. Us? No way. No, siree.

Crab Definitely not.

Her Very well then. It's a deal. A girl it shall be. And I'll make her work like she's never worked before. I'll make her chop the wood, and build the fire, and grind the millet, and fetch the water...

Cat Yes, Mum, we know.

Dog We've been through all that before.

Crab And some.

Her Less cheek, and more action. The right girl still

hasn't showed up yet! And until she does, you know what your tasks are.

All Yes, Mum.

Her Then vanish, and graft, and weep! My bottomless calabash awaits your bitter tears.

*Enter **Anansi** dressed ridiculously as a young woman.*

Anansi The things you have to do to get a job these days.

Her Aha! You must be the girl!

Anansi That's me, Ma'am.

Her Well, let's see you curtsy, then.

***Anansi** tries and looks ridiculous.*

Her That's not a very ladylike curtsy.

Anansi I know, Ma'am, I'm sorry. It's been so long, and I have a slight problem with my legs.

Her And what would that be? Your legs need to be tough and quick if you're to work for me.

Anansi Oh, they're tough and quick, alright, Ma'am. All of them...

Her Pardon?

Anansi When do I start, Ma'am?

Her NOW! Chop the wood... fetch the water...

*This speeds up until **Anansi** is mixed up and weeping.*

...and back to fetching water. And don't forget to leave your tears in the calabash on the way out. I'm working up a mighty thirst just watching you.

2 At the River

Anansi A week of this and I'll be knackered. I don't know how you put up with this, mate.

Crab Knackered? That's not a very ladylike word from a sweet little thing like you.

Anansi Hm! OH! Kind sir, if only you knew what she puts me through...

Crab There, there...

Anansi BOO HOO! Woe is me! How will I ever survive until the end of the week?

Crab Why? What happens at the end of the week?

Anansi Didn't you hear? I won't get paid unless I can guess the old ratbag's real name.

Crab The old what?

Anansi My gracious employer's real name...

Crab Well, that's easy for me, of course... pet... 'cos she's my Mum.

Anansi She is?

Crab Yes... sweetheart... that's right.

Anansi But how, oh how can that help me?

Crab Because I know her real name, see, my little sweetie.

Anansi Oh, you naughty, naughty, NAUGHTY man! You don't!

Crab I do... darlin'

Anansi Don't.

Crab Yes I do... petal.

Anansi Don't, don't, don't.

Crab Give us a kiss.

ANANSI Name first, or I'll slug you one.

Crab whispers something to Anansi.

ANANSI Really? I might have guessed. Well... no point knocking around here when I could be splitting the old girl's loot.

CRAB Hold on a minute.

ANANSI What?

CRAB Aren't you forgetting something?

ANANSI Oh... yeah... (*Gets kiss.*) Well. I've had worse. See you.

HER Girl. Where have you been?

ANANSI I'd like to claim my wages now, Ma'am.

HER But your work isn't finished yet! My calabash is empty!

ANANSI Well, you won't be needing that where you're going to, because I know your real name.

HER But... that's impossible.

ANANSI No, it isn't.

HER Try me, then.

ANANSI Your real name is... LILLIBET!

She freezes.

Am I right or am I right?

She nods.

OK, then, half the stuff and make it snappy.
Half the bottle of rum...
Not the empty half, the full half...
Now put it in a paper bag...
Not half a paper bag, dummy...
OK, put in half of a PAIR of paper bags...
That's better. Now the socks...

On second thoughts, forget it...
So. That'll be it then.
Lizzy.
Bess.
Bessie.
Lill.
Betty.
Lillibet.
Elizabeth.
Ma'am.

HER That's enough! Don't rub it in! Just GO!

Off he goes.

ANANSI Hard work's to blame
I've got no shame
I got her number and I won her game.

HER Children! Come here at once! You can see how I've been humiliated! Now which one of you told that... that strange looking girl my name?

Come along, now, own up. I can wait here all day. Own up now and it'll be a lot easier on all of you.

CRAB It was me, Mum.

HER (*Shrieks.*) You... you... CRUSTACEAN!

GIRL And she threw the empty calabash at Crab, and all the tears that all her slaves had ever cried made it stick, hard and fast, to his back. And hard work and a hard back have been stuck together with tears ever since.

That's what my story's going to be: a hard back, many tears and a name that nobody knows. A new story for a new world.

She steps back into the auction scene, which comes back to life. She doesn't look frightened any more.

KINGSTON HARBOUR

Auctioneer SOLD!

Girl Once upon a time there was a girl who got taken away. She lives in a story that never seems to end. Remember her.

Auctioneer SOLD!

ACTIVITIES

Things to talk about

1 Alistair Campbell shows us two very different worlds in *Anansi*. One is the dark and terrifying world of the slave ship. The other the bizarre and colourful Forest of Stories.

- What effect did jumping from one dimension to the other have on you as you read the play through?
- What do you think these contrasts add to the play? Do they make anything clearer or did they confuse you?

2 It's not just the settings of the story that contrast with each other.

- In what ways are the Captain and the Boy, and the Woman and the Girl, similar and different?
- How does the relationship between these characters develop through the play? Are they the same at the end as they were at the beginning? If they have changed, how have they?
- How does contrasting these characters tell the audience something?

3 At the end of the play the Girl tells a story of her own. She tells it directly to the audience.

- What does the Girl's story tell us about her?
- How do you suppose the audience would react to being spoken to directly by the Girl at the end? How would they feel about her?

4 Anansi is a strange kind of hero. Unlike many heroes in stories he certainly doesn't just do good things for other people. Talk about:

- what you think makes Anansi an interesting character;

- his strengths and weaknesses;
- whether he teaches the Girl some good things, even though he might not be entirely 'good' himself;
- whether you agree with the opinion that children should only be told stories about 'good' characters, so that they will have role models to look up to.

5 **WOMAN** *You do have a mother.*

GIRL *But she isn't here.*

WOMAN *Africa is your mother.*

- What do you think the Woman means when she says this?
- As the play goes on, the Girl begins to call the Woman 'Mother'. Do you think the Woman represents Africa in any way?
- If the Woman does *symbolise* Africa, what do you think it means when she is thrown overboard?

THINGS TO WRITE ABOUT

6 Look at the chart below. It gives some ideas for different pieces of writing.

- Working in pairs, choose any two of the ideas which you think will make a strong contrast. Alternatively, you could think of two pieces of your own.
- Write the two pieces out.
- Now find a way of presenting them. Perhaps you will decide to cut from one to the other then back again, in order to make the most of the contrasts.
- Talk about how you can get a powerful dramatic effect by contrasting pieces of writing in this way.

The Girl has kept a secret diary on the voyage. How does she report the death of the Woman?	The Boy is called to give evidence against his father who is tried for his part in the trade. What is his statement?
The Boy slips the Girl a letter when she is taken off the ship in the Indies. What does it say?	The Girl writes out a new Anansi story which she reads to the children of her owner. What's the story?
What entry did the Captain makes in his log on the day he was hired to pick up his first cargo of slaves?	What prayer does the Captain's wife say for him while he is away?

7 Imagine that, when the Boy returns to England after his first voyage, he is sent a letter by the company that owns the ship. Here is the start of the letter:.

Messrs. Rochester and Cosway
Shipping Agents
21 Cable Street, Bristol

Dear Sir

Our first duty is to offer our most sincere condolences on the loss of your dear father. He was an outstanding example to us all, and doubtless taught you a great deal about trade and manhood. Your courage and fortitude on the return from Jamaica was notable, and it is now our pleasure to offer you a position on a second voyage to Africa and thence to the Indies, with a similar cargo. On this voyage, though, you will be no lowly cabin boy but afforded the status of Junior Officer.

- Jot down as many ideas as you can about what the Boy might think as a result of receiving this letter.
- Now write his reply.

8 Choose one of the characters from the ship scenes. Draw a rough outline of the character.

- Inside the outline, jot down words which describe what you think the character is like.
- Draw a speech balloon coming from the character's head. In it write a line of your own that you think would be a typical sort of thing for them to say.
- Now draw a 'thinks bubble' and write in it what they might really be thinking at the same moment.

9 In groups of four, cast yourselves as the Girl, Boy, Captain and Woman.

- Find a way of positioning yourselves which clearly shows who is who and what you think about each other.
- Now think about how you might walk onto the stage in order to get into this position.
- Add no more than three or four small movements or gestures to the tableau which could tell an audience more about the characters and their relationships.
- Finally, find a way of getting off the stage which contrasts with the entrance but adds to the meanings you have already created.
- Share and discuss your work.

10 Look at the first and last speeches the Girl makes.

- Jot down your ideas on how the speeches are different.
- Rehearse the two speeches and think about how you can use your voice and your body to show

that the Girl's character has changed.

11 Pick out four lines from the play which you think sum up the character of the Captain. For example:

The only story that counts, young man. The story that says money makes the world go round.

- Think about what other characters the Captain may have in his life. A wife? The people who own the ship? Sailors who think he is a good skipper – or some who think he is not. Pick a character such as this, and think of at least two questions that character would like to ask the Captain.
- Hot-seat either your teacher or a volunteer in the role of the Captain. When you ask your questions, try to make it clear who you are, what role you are taking.
- Discuss how this sort of exercise might help actors when they prepare to play parts on stage.

12 Finding a way of playing the different animals in the Forest of Stories is both fun and challenging.

- Pick a line for one of the following characters that you think is really typical of them:

  Anansi Tiger Snake Ratbat

- Practise saying the line on your own. Try the line quickly and slowly, softly and loudly, deeply or squeakily. Try lots of combinations until you find one that you feel is just right.
- Now put some movement into your character. Again try different things. Does the character have sharp, darting movements or slow, deliberate ones?
- Move around the room in your character and say your line to everyone you meet. Can you pick

out other people who have chosen the same character as you, even though they may have chosen different lines? How could you tell?

13 What sounds might the captives have heard as they lay in the hold of the slave ship?

- As a whole class, build up a *soundscape* of the ship using your voices and perhaps hands to capture the slapping of the waves, the creaking of the boards, the quiet moans of the captives and maybe the muffled cries of the sailors on the deck above.
- Now spread out around the space. Set up the soundscape again but add a simple, repetitive movement. The aim is to try and find a way of setting the atmosphere for the audience in an interesting, theatrical way, using your bodies instead of relying on a recorded soundtrack.
- Try to create an image for the Forest of Stories in the same way.
- Talk about the different, contrasting effects you have managed to achieve.

14 In small groups, choose part of a scene that you think could be quite distressing for the audience. Compare it to one that you think they would find funny.

- Rehearse the two scenes, either using the script or by improvising your own words.
- Act out the two scenes, putting the distressing one first, then moving straight into the comic one.
- Now try it the other way around.
- Talk about the different effects the different orders might have on an audience.

15 No poster was designed for the original production of *Anansi*. If you were to produce the play in your school, what images would you want to include on the poster? Think about the dark story of the Girl's voyage on the slave ship, but also about how the Anansi stories are lively and give her hope.

Staging the play

16 In what way is the Woman different from the other characters?

- In groups of three or four, try out the scene on pages 12–14. Two of you should play the scene and the others watch. Try the scene in two different ways: first, so that the audience can clearly see both the Girl and the Woman, then so they can only partly see the Woman (perhaps just her back).
- Talk about the different effects you achieved. What might be added to the scene by not allowing the audience to see the Woman clearly?

17

- Make a list of all the different locations shown in the play.
- What would be the practical difficulties of changing the set for every new scene?

In the original production of *Anansi*, Breakout Theatre Company used a very simple but effective set. A large *floor cloth* was painted with the outlines of figures packed closely together as if they were in the hold of a slave ship. In the centre of the stage stood a thick wooden mast with two or three wooden beams angled against it. A net was stretched from the mast to the stage cloth. This gave a good impression of the ship. For the Forest of Stories scenes, brightly coloured leaves were added to the structure, and the net seemed to change from suggesting ship's rigging to suggesting a spider's web. This is called a *composite set*.

- What would be the advantages of having just one simple design which could be altered in slight ways to suggest different locations?
- Try to sketch the set described above, or alternatively design one of your own for this play.

18 A particularly interesting design problem in *Anansi* is how to show the characters in the stories.

- Talk about the advantages and disadvantages of having elaborate costumes which make the animals look real.
- How might you suggest the different animals in a simpler, and perhaps more effective, way? Think about how you might use:
  - make-up
  - masks
  - props
  - simple pieces of costume

THE SLAVE TRADE

Slaves work for no money. They are the property of another person and may be bought and sold. They have no rights. Two hundred years ago British ports such as Liverpool and Bristol became rich as a result of the slave trade. In America and the West Indies, white plantation owners became immensely wealthy by using slaves.

Some white people believed that treating Africans in this way was perfectly all right because they could not think or feel like 'real' (white) humans.Their image of Africans as being simple savages was, however, very far from the truth.

19 The novelist Philippa Gregory did a great deal of research for her book *A Respectable Trade*, which tells the story of how the young wife of a Bristol slave trader comes to realise her own ignorance as she teaches a slave, Mehuru, how to speak English. Read these short extracts from the book:

Mehuru, dressed very fine in a long embroidered gown of indigo silk and with a staff in his hand carved with Snake, his personal guardian deity, strolled up the hill to the palace of Old Oyo with Siko walking behind him.

It was yet another full meeting of the council in two long months of meetings. The Alafin – the king – was on his throne, his mother seated behind him. The head of the military was there, his scarred face turning everywhere, always suspicious. The council, whose responsibility was for law and enforcement throughout the wide federation of the Yoruba Empire, was all there; and Mehuru's immediate superior, the high priest, was on his stool.

Mehuru slipped in and stood at the priest's shoulder. The debate had been going on for months; it was of such importance that no-one wanted to hurry the decision. But a consensus was slowly emerging.

'We need the guns,' the old soldier said briefly. 'We have to trade with the white men to buy the guns we need. Without guns and cannon I cannot guarantee the security of the kingdom. The kingdom of Dahomey, which has traded slaves for guns, is fast becoming the greatest of all. I warn you: they will come against us one day, and without guns of our own we cannot survive.

She did not think about where he had come from. She had no notion of an Africa before the coming of the British, of a huge continent populated by a complex of different peoples and kingdoms, of trading and barter stations, of caravans of goods which crossed from one nation to another: of men and women, some living like peasants working the land, some living in towns and cities and working in industries, some established in hereditary kingdoms seated on thrones of gold and ivory and living like gods.

'You have learned much quicker than the others,' Francis observed.

'I like different languages,' Mehuru explained slowly, 'I speak four African languages, and a little Portuguese. Until I came to England I thought that all white men spoke Portuguese. English is not very different from Portuguese. Some of the words are the same, as you must know.'

'I don't speak Portuguese,' Francis confessed. 'Just French, and a little Italian.'

'You are very ignorant then,' Mehuru said with provocative impertinence.

- How do you think African slaves are generally represented in stories and films?
- Talk about how the images in these extracts from Philippa Gregory's novel create a very different impression.

One of the best-known traditions of West Indian culture is *limbo dancing*. To the rhythm of a steel band, the dancers try their skill at moving under a low bar without letting their hands or back touch the ground.

The dance is a celebration; it is part of the fun of carnival, and gives the performers a chance to show their energy, suppleness and strength. But where did the dance originate?

20 Read this poem by Edward Kamau Brathwaite:

Limbo

And the limbo stick is the silence in front of me
limbo

limbo
limbo like me
limbo
limbo like me

long dark night is the silence in front of me
limbo
limbo like me
stick hit sound
and the ship like it ready

limbo
limbo like me

long dark deck and the water surrounding me
long dark deck and the silence is over me

limbo
limbo like me
stick is the whip
and the dark deck is slavery

stick is the whip
and the dark deck is slavery

limbo
limbo like me
drum stick knocks
and the darkness is over me

knees spread wide
and the water is hiding me

limbo
limbo like me
knees spread wide
and the dark ground is under me

down
down
down

and the drummer is calling me
limbo
limbo like me

sun coming up
and the drummers are praising me

out of the dark
and the dumb gods are raising me

up
up
up
and the music is saving me

hot slow
step
on the limbo ground

The poem makes the limbo dance seem like the voyage from Africa. There is a fear of the unknown, then a struggle to survive. Finally there is the celebration of passing the test.

The word 'limbo' can be used to describe a place which is neither one thing nor another, a place of waiting to see what will happen next. Perhaps Limbo is the place between Heaven and Hell.

- In groups, work on a presentation of the poem. Try to match the rhythm of the words to the movement of the dance.
- In larger groups, you could contrast your presentation of the poem with a number of background images showing its origins: the beating of the captives onto the ship; the cramped conditions in the hold; the way the captives had to move. (The gap between the decks was very small in order to pack as many people onto the ship as possible. It has been suggested that the limbo dance comes from the way the captives tried to keep themselves fit and supple by moving around in the same way as dancers now go under the stick). Finally you might show an image of the captives emerging into the sunlight of the West Indies – they are still slaves, but they have survived.

FURTHER WORK

21 What might the Girl's life have been like before she was captured?

- In groups, make a series of five tableaux which show different aspects of her life.
- Now find a way of moving smoothly from one to the next.
- Finally, add either a spoken description or musical background to your work which would help an audience understand her life better.

22 In groups, try to find a way of showing how the Girl and the Woman were captured. Think about what effect you want the scene to have on the audience. It could be quite a shocking contrast to the work you created above.

23 When the Woman is dragged away, the Boy lingers and says 'You mustn't cry.'

- In pairs, imagine that the Boy and Girl can speak the same language. Carry on their conversation from this point.
- Find a strong way of ending the conversation. Perhaps there will be a particularly powerful line, or you may decide to freeze the picture at a certain point.
- Share your work and discuss what makes a powerful ending to a scene.

24 Re-read Anansi's rap on page 17. Make up a rap of your own which tells the story of the Girl's voyage to the West Indies. The rap should use rhyme and have a strong rhythm.

Tape-record or share your work by presenting it out loud to see how well the rhythm works.

25 In groups, improvise one of the following scenes. Try to use silences and looks to suggest what the characters are thinking and feeling, rather than launching into arguments.

- The Girl is sold to a family who later move to England, where she is freed. One day, she meets the Captain's son, who now has a ship of his own.
- On a later voyage to the West Indies, the Captain is taken seriously ill. He is sent to a hospital in Kingston in Jamaica where the Girl is now helping to care for the patients.
- The Captain and his son return to Africa to pick up another cargo of slaves. On the quayside is a Woman. The Boy notices that there is something about her that is frighteningly familiar. How does he tell his father this?

26 Imagine that the Girl lives to be a very old woman. Think about how her life may have changed. Perhaps she does not die a slave at all, but has gone on to do great things.

As she lies dying, what images from her past would float into her mind?

- In groups, or as a whole class, gather together ideas about the different characters she may remember. They might be ones from her real life or perhaps characters from the stories she was told.
- Choose a character for yourself. Make up a line (or choose one from the play) that you think would have burned its way into the Girl's mind.
- Find a way of making a scene which would show an audience how the Girl, as an old woman, is remembering these things. How would you

move? How might you say the lines aloud? Perhaps the group could create a quiet background soundscape to *underscore* the lines being spoken and add to the atmosphere.

27 In small groups, devise three short scenes which show what the Boy's life is like five years after his first voyage; then ten years after; and when he is an old man.

- How do you suppose his life might contrast with that of the Girl?
- Devise two contrasting still images which show how the Girl and the Boy turn out as adults. Try to show what the strengths and qualities of their characters are in your images.